Look 🚢 🚂 Puzzle ✈️ 🚌 Learn

The Great World Tour

Kamini Khanduri

Illustrated by
David Hancock

Series editor: Felicity Brooks

Contents

SCHOLASTIC INC.
New York Toronto London Auckland Sydney
Mexico City New Delhi Hong Kong

About this book

Great Aunt Marigold has given you a wonderful present: a ticket to go on a Great World Tour. You will visit lots of exciting places and there are all kinds of things to find and puzzles to solve along the way.

This is Great Aunt Marigold. She'll be coming with you on the tour.

This map of the world shows the places you will stop at on your tour.

Great Aunt Marigold says that in each place, you have to pick up a present for a friend or relation. But she hasn't told you which present is in which place – that's one of the puzzles for you to solve. Here's what you have to find:

Iceland
Siberia
USA
The Alps
Greece
Japan
Morocco
China
Middle East
Trinidad
East Africa
India
Amazon Rainforest
Thailand
Australia
The Antarctic

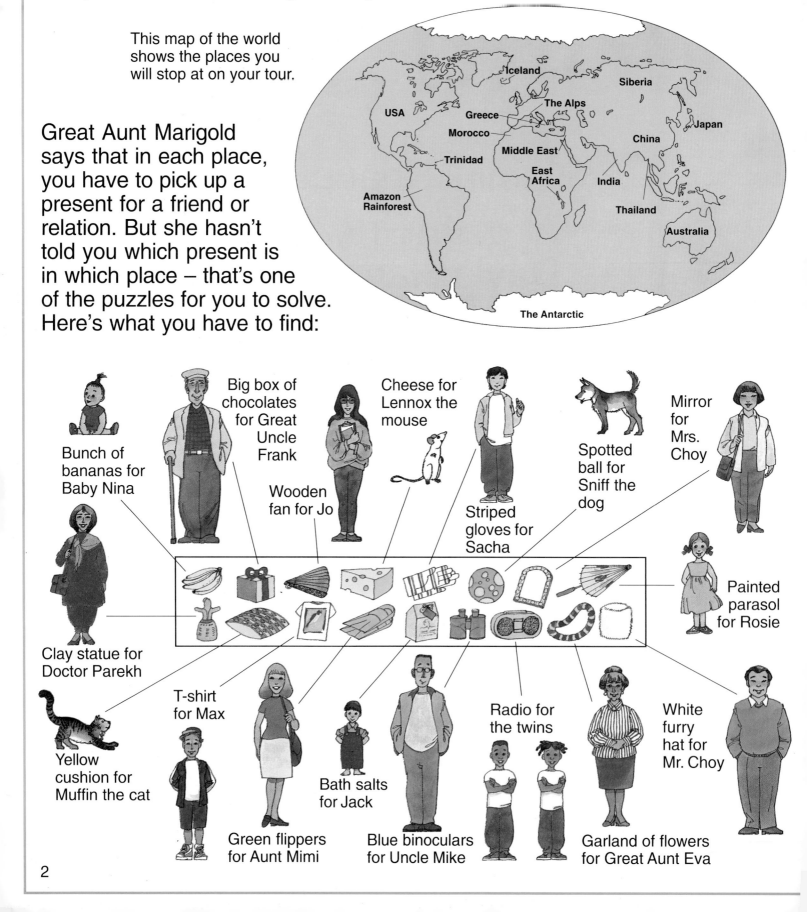

Bunch of bananas for Baby Nina

Big box of chocolates for Great Uncle Frank

Cheese for Lennox the mouse

Spotted ball for Sniff the dog

Mirror for Mrs. Choy

Wooden fan for Jo

Striped gloves for Sacha

Painted parasol for Rosie

Clay statue for Doctor Parekh

Yellow cushion for Muffin the cat

T-shirt for Max

Bath salts for Jack

Radio for the twins

White furry hat for Mr. Choy

Green flippers for Aunt Mimi

Blue binoculars for Uncle Mike

Garland of flowers for Great Aunt Eva

What to spot

Each of the double pages in this book shows a different place on your tour. In each place, there are lots of things to look for. Some things are easy to spot, but some are very tricky. This is how the puzzles work.

These little pictures show the things you can find in the big picture.

This strip tells you where you are, what time it is, and what the weather's like.

This tells you what Great Aunt Marigold is doing. You'll find her in every place.

This box is a reminder of the presents you have to find. There's one present in each place.

The writing next to each little picture tells you how many of that thing to look for in the big picture.

Even if you can only see part of a thing, it still counts.

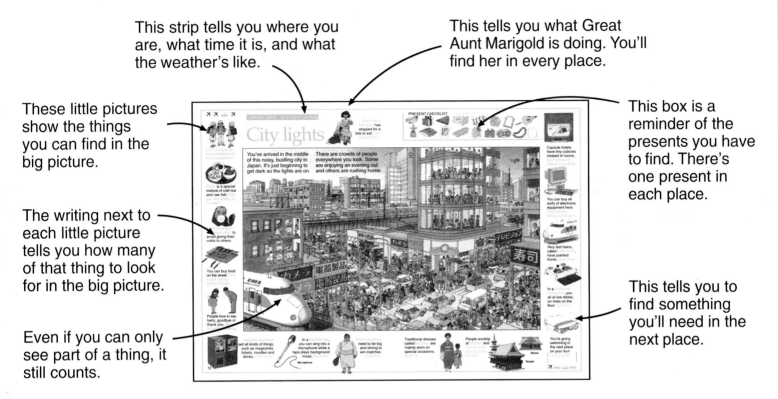

This tells you to find something you'll need in the next place.

Finding the way

When you've done all the puzzles on a double page, you have to find out where to go to next – it won't be the place on the next page in the book. You also need to find how to travel there. Here's what you do.

In the bottom right-hand corner of each double page, four tiny pictures tell you how to travel to the next place.

To find out where to go next, look for exactly the same four pictures in the top left-hand corner of another double page.

You'll travel by train, plane, boat or bus, but you won't use them all on each journey, and you may use any of them more than once.

PUZZLE CHECKLIST

In each place, you must find:
* Great Aunt Marigold
* One present for a friend or relation
* Lots of things hidden in the big picture
* One thing you'll need in the next place
* Which place to go to next

If you get stuck finding your way, there's a map showing the correct route on page 40. If you get stuck doing any of the other puzzles, you'll find all the answers on pages 42-47. Now turn the page to begin your Great World Tour...

At the airport

Great Aunt Marigold has lots of bags. Find her.

Information about flights is displayed on screens. Can you spot 11?

You can shop for all kinds of things. Find someone buying sunglasses.

To get onto the plane, you go along a covered walkway. Can you see where it is?

Restaurants serve food and drink. Can you spot someone eating this meal?

Old or disabled people can be driven around in buggies. Spot two.

You're setting off on your exciting world tour from a big, busy airport. Outside, the plane is already filling up with people. Before getting on board, you must check in your bags and go through security. Then you'll be off!

Some kinds of pets can be taken on planes, but only in special containers. Find this cat.

Bag being searched

Knife showing up on X-ray machine

Security officers check that no one has any weapons. Find these things.

Person going through metal detector

4

Bags that have been checked in are loaded into the cargo hold of the plane. Find it.

You need a ticket to go on a plane journey. Spot someone who has torn his ticket.

You can wheel your bags around on a trolley. Can you spot seven?

At the bureau de change, you can buy money to use in other countries. Can you find it?

Phone. Spot eight.

Flight attendants look after the passengers on planes. Find ten.

Officers in the control tower give instructions to the pilots of the planes. Can you see it?

In the first place on your tour, there's going to be a festival. Find a red flag to wave.

Floating market

Great Aunt Marigold is dropping her shopping. Find her.

A straw hat will protect you from the sun. Spot two boats selling hats.

Most fruit and vegetables are sold by weight. Spot nine sets of weighing scales.

Can you find 11 purple-throated sunbirds?

You can buy curry with noodles or rice. Find two boats where food is being cooked and sold.

You've taken a trip along a canal to visit this unusual market. Most things here are being sold from boats. If you want to buy something, just call out to the person in the boat. She'll paddle over and you can do your shopping.

Can you spot someone who is selling grilled corn on the cob?

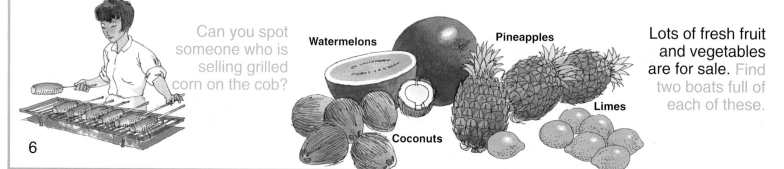

Watermelons

Pineapples

Coconuts

Limes

Lots of fresh fruit and vegetables are for sale. Find two boats full of each of these.

6

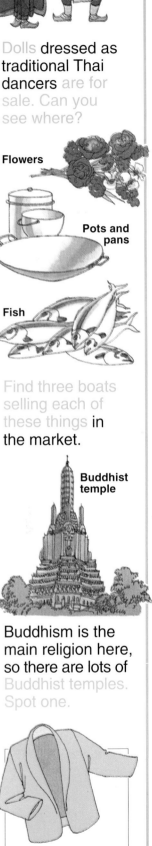

Dolls dressed as traditional Thai dancers are for sale. Can you see where?

Flowers

Pots and pans

Fish

Find three boats selling each of these things in the market.

Buddhist temple

Buddhism is the main religion here, so there are lots of Buddhist temples. Spot one.

You can buy all kinds of beautiful handmade crafts. Can you spot these things?

Carved wooden tables

Embroidered cushions

Silver necklaces

Lacquerware ducks

Buddhist monks come out of their temples to ask for food. Spot six.

In the next place, you'll be going out for the evening. Find this silk jacket to wear.

On the beach

Great Aunt Marigold is being very active. Can you see her?

Windsurfers sail along, standing on a sailboard. Find ten.

Sunblock

Sunblock protects your skin from the sun. Spot four people putting it on.

Dolphins are very friendly and often swim near people. Spot ten.

Kayak

Speedboat

Sailboat

There are all kinds of boats here. Find seven of each of these.

Spot 14 seagulls.

It's a hot, sunny summer's day and you've arrived at a very crowded beach. You could go for a swim, or join all the people doing exciting sports in the water. If you're feeling lazy, you could just lie on the sand and relax.

Water-skiers are pulled along on the surface of the water by a speedboat. Spot eight.

Teams of lifesavers look out for people in danger. Spot a team doing a practice rescue.

You can go diving around coral reefs to look at the amazing underwater wildlife. Spot five divers.

PRESENT CHECKLIST

Flags mark out which areas are safe from sharks or dangerous tides. Spot two.

Koala

Kangaroo

Kangaroos and koalas live in the wild in Australia. Can you find a toy one of each?

Surfers skim over the waves on a surfboard. Find 30.

People drive jet skis across the water. Spot nine.

In the next place, there are some unusual birds. Find a camera to photograph them.

You can breathe through a snorkel when you swim with your face in the water. Spot ten snorkels.

Snorkel

Parasailers have parachutes. A boat pulls them along on the water and they rise into the air. Spot two.

The Bedouin take good care of their camels and often give them names. Can you spot 40?

Bedouin foods include meat, rice, cheese and bread. Find someone baking bread.

These musical instruments, called rababs are often played to entertain guests. Find four.

Goats are kept for meat, and their thick hair is woven to make tents. Spot 30.

Desert homes

Great Aunt Marigold is being helpful. Can you see where she is?

You've journeyed across the dry, dusty desert to visit the Bedouin people. They usually live in small groups, but today they've come together to prepare for a big festival. The tents are buzzing with all kinds of activity.

In each tent, the men's area and the women's area are separated by a curtain, called a sahah. Find four.

Sahah

Sacks of dried food

Strings of onions

The Bedouin sell animals and buy some things at markets in towns. Find three of each of these things.

Metal cooking pots

Women weave rugs, saddlebags, cushions and cloth from goat or camel hair. Find this rug.

Today, most Bedouin travel in trucks instead of on camels. Can you find nine?

Fast dogs, called salukis, hunt hares for their owners. Spot ten.

People drink frothy camel milk and also use it for cooking. Spot three bowls of it.

In the next place, you can visit temples. Spot a book telling you where they are.

The Bedouin make coffee for anyone who visits their tent. Find these things.

Coffee pot

Ladle for roasting coffee

Pestle and mortar for grinding coffee

Coffee cups

Can you find three camel saddles?

City lights

Great Aunt Marigold has stopped for a bite to eat. Can you find her?

Can you spot 20 schoolchildren with their backpacks?

Sushi is a special mixture of cold rice and raw fish. Can you see where it's for sale?

Spot six people wearing masks to avoid giving their colds to others.

You can buy food on the street. Find a stall selling grilled chicken.

People bow to say hello, goodbye or thank you. Spot 14 people bowing.

You've arrived in the middle of this noisy, bustling city in Japan. It's just beginning to get dark so the lights are on.

There are crowds of people everywhere you look. Some are enjoying an evening out and others are rushing home.

Vending machines sell all kinds of things, such as magazines, tickets, noodles and drinks. Find seven.

In a karaoke bar, you can sing into a microphone while a tape plays background music. Spot one.

Microphone

Sumo wrestlers need to be big and strong to win matches. Find four.

PRESENT CHECKLIST

Capsule hotels have tiny cubicles instead of rooms. Spot someone asleep in a cubicle.

You can buy all sorts of electronic equipment here. Find a place selling computers.

Very fast trains, called bullet trains have pointed fronts. Spot three.

In a traditional restaurant, you sit at low tables, on mats on the floor. Spot one.

You're going swimming in the next place on your tour. Find a towel.

Traditional dresses called kimonos are mainly worn on special occasions. Spot 16.

People worship at temples and shrines. Can you spot one of each?

Shrine

Temple

At the pool

Great Aunt Marigold is trying to read. Can you see where she is?

All kinds of birds make their nests on nearby coasts. Spot 20 eider ducks.

Toy shark

Inflatable bed

Many people just come to relax and have fun in the water. Find seven of each of these.

Floating buoys show you where the water's too hot to swim in, and where it's very shallow. Spot 20.

A power station next to the pool uses steam from the hot water. Can you find five pipes blowing out steam?

Horse riding

You can have fun splashing around in this pool called the Blue Lagoon. The hot, salty water comes up from under the ground. Nearby, there are bubbling mud pools and springs that spout steam and boiling water into the air.

There are lots of activities to do in the area. Spot seven people doing each of these things.

Hiking

At the Blue Lagoon Clinic, doctors treat people who have skin problems. Can you see a doctor?

Skincare products are for sale here. Find someone who has bought lots of tubes of face cream.

Trucks are good for driving on Iceland's bumpy roads. Spot eight.

These food trays contain Icelandic fish, such as shark, shrimp or salmon. Spot 21.

There are changing rooms where you can leave your clothes. Find the women's one.

You can stay at the Blue Lagoon Hotel. Spot a man who's just arrived with lots of bags.

Waiters and waitresses serve people food and drink in the water. Spot four of each.

Both the water, and the mud at the bottom of the pool are supposed to be good for your skin. Spot 15 people with mud on their faces.

Next, you're going on a boat. Find some sea-sickness pills in case you feel ill.

Frozen land

Great Aunt Marigold is wrapped up warmly. Can you see her?

Albatrosses glide over the water looking for food. Find three.

No one lives here all the time, but scientists stay at the research station. Find it.

Killer whales sometimes hunt seals by tipping them off pieces of ice. Spot four.

Castle

Pyramid

Greek temple

Icebergs are huge lumps of ice that float in the sea. Can you find these different shapes?

You've come to the cold, windy Antarctic, where the land and sea are nearly always frozen. You can watch whales and take photos of penguins, but you mustn't disturb the animals or spoil their icy home.

"Porpoising" out of the water

"Tobogganing" across the ice

Penguins can't fly, but they have other ways of moving fast. Find 12 penguins doing each of these things.

Scientists dive into the icy water to watch animals and take pictures. Find seven divers.

Crabeater seal. Spot 12.

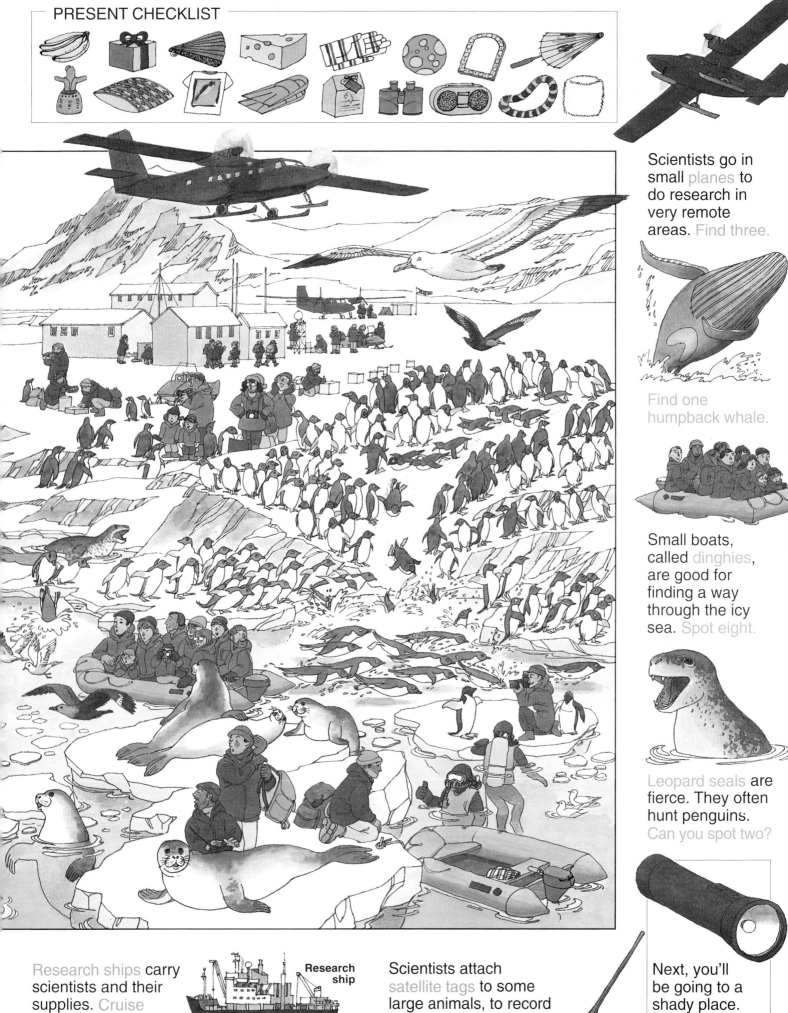

Scientists go in small planes to do research in very remote areas. Find three.

Find one humpback whale.

Small boats, called dinghies, are good for finding a way through the icy sea. Spot eight.

Leopard seals are fierce. They often hunt penguins. Can you spot two?

Next, you'll be going to a shady place. Find a flashlight to help you see.

Research ships carry scientists and their supplies. Cruise ships carry tourists. Spot one of each.

Research ship

Cruise ship

Scientists attach satellite tags to some large animals, to record information about how they live. Spot two.

Carnival!

PRESENT CHECKLIST

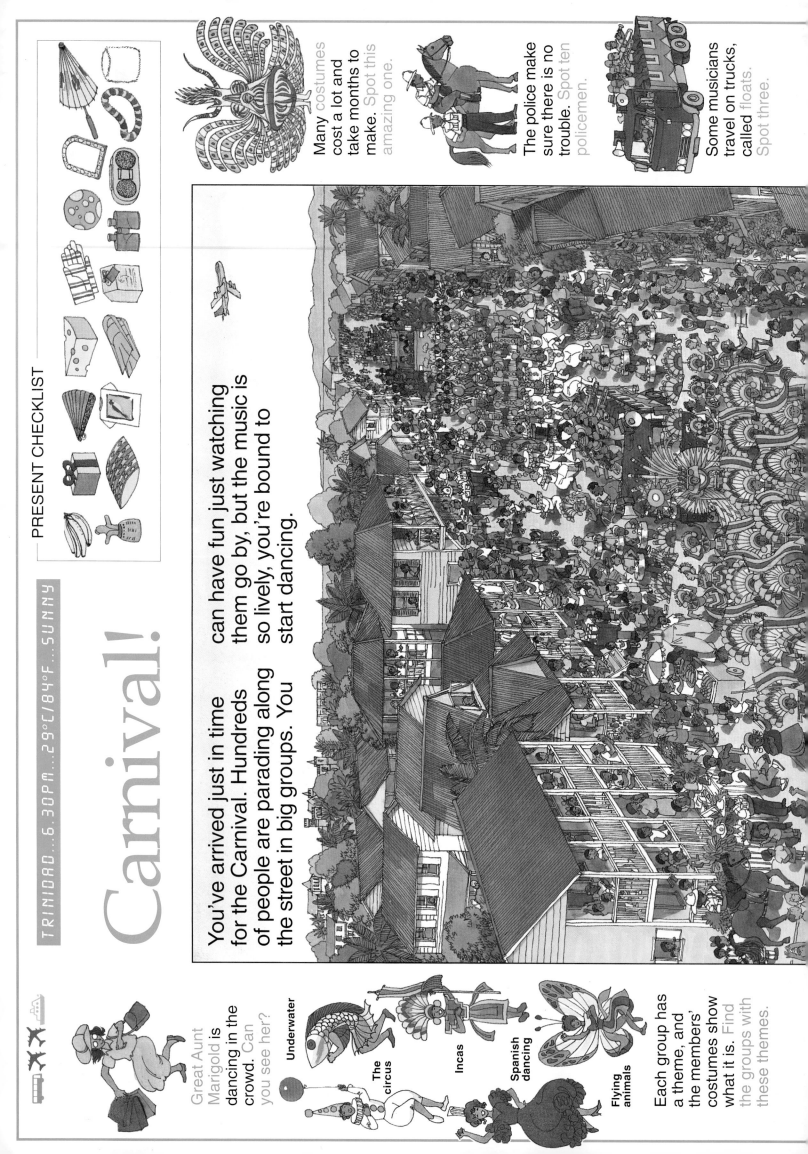

You've arrived just in time for the Carnival. Hundreds of people are parading along the street in big groups. You can have fun just watching them go by, but the music is so lively, you're bound to start dancing.

Many costumes cost a lot and take months to make. Spot this amazing one.

The police make sure there is no trouble. Spot ten policemen.

Some musicians travel on trucks, called floats. Spot three.

Great Aunt Marigold is dancing in the crowd. Can you see her?

Underwater

The circus

Incas

Spanish dancing

Flying animals

Each group has a theme, and the members' costumes show what it is. Find the groups with these themes.

These metal drums are called pans. Spot 18.

Moco Jumbie

Burroquite

Jab Molassi

Some traditional characters are here every year. Find these.

Next, you'll be doing lots of shopping. Find a calculator to add up what you spend.

Tasty tropical fruits, such as mangoes and pineapples, grow in Trinidad. Find a fruit stall.

Carnival songs, called calypsos, have a strong beat and are good to dance to. Spot two people singing into microphones.

The coconut seller slices the top off the coconut, so you can drink the juice and scoop out the soft, white flesh. Find her.

Cups of fruit sorbet

Corn on the cob

Bread called roti

Can you see where people are selling these snacks on the street?

Judges decide which group has the best music and costumes. Spot someone pretending to be a judge.

19

Shady souk

Great Aunt Marigold is buying all kinds of things. Can you see her?

Herbs and spices, such as mint and saffron, look and smell wonderful. Find where they are being sold.

Lute

Drum

You can often hear music in the souk. Find these instruments.

Wool for making carpets is dyed and hung up to dry. Spot three people carrying bundles of wool.

Dates grow in the desert, on date palm trees. Can you see some dates for sale?

Painted pottery

Woven baskets

Copper trays

Leather slippers called babouches

Embroidered caps

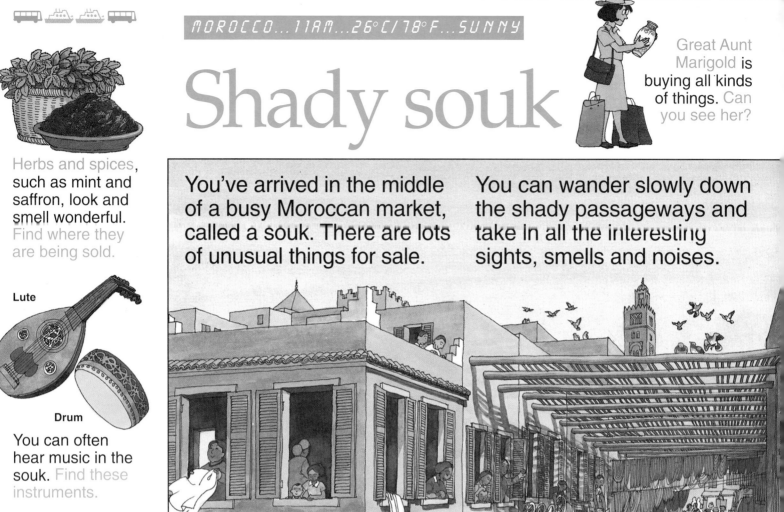

You've arrived in the middle of a busy Moroccan market, called a souk. There are lots of unusual things for sale.

You can wander slowly down the shady passageways and take in all the interesting sights, smells and noises.

You can buy lovely handmade crafts and may even see some being made. Find where these things are being sold.

Horse riding has been popular here for hundreds of years. Spot two saddles for sale.

PRESENT CHECKLIST

Water carriers go around selling cups of water to thirsty shoppers. Spot four.

Live animals are on sale. Find nine chickens.

People argue over the price of things. Spot two people bargaining for this carpet.

Can you spot where olives are being sold from huge baskets?

In the next place, you might sit out in the hot sun. Find a shady hat to wear.

While you are deciding what to buy, the stall holder may offer you a glass of hot mint tea. Spot seven.

Women buy powder for making up their eyes, lips and cheeks, and cedarwood containers to keep it in. Spot 12.

Cedarwood container

Bottles of powder

At the mall

Great Aunt Marigold has bought lots of things. Can you find her?

There are plenty of benches to sit on if you get tired. Spot eight.

At the information desk, people will help you find what you need. Can you see it?

The mall is so big, it's easy to get lost. Find a child who has lost his mother.

You can have your hair washed and cut at the hair salon. Can you spot it?

At this big, busy mall, you can do all your shopping without ever having to go outside. If you don't want to shop, you can eat or drink instead. Some people come to the mall to meet their friends and have a chat.

Kites

Sports equipment

Cowboy hats

Books

Flowers

Shoes

Jeans

Cakes

Can you find where these things are for sale?

Can you spot a group of cheerleaders putting on a show?

PRESENT CHECKLIST

Paintings, called murals, make the walls look bright and interesting. Can you see one?

You can travel from one level to another in the glass elevator. Can you find it?

Spot five telephones.

Security guards check that there is no trouble in the mall. Spot ten.

In the next place, you might stay in a hotel. Find a new suitcase to put your things in.

You can buy lots of different food here. Can you see where people are eating these things?

Spaghetti

Pizza

Ice cream

Statues, plants and fountains make you feel as if you're outside. Spot 24 flamingo statues.

Going skiing

Snowmobiles are like little cars on skis. Spot five.

Goggles protect your eyes from the sun. Can you see someone who has broken his goggles?

Chairlift

Gondola

Chairlifts and gondolas take you to the top of steep slopes. Find four of each of these.

You can ride through the snow in a horse-drawn sleigh. Spot three.

Great Aunt Marigold isn't a very good skier. Can you see where she is?

This crowded ski resort is one of the liveliest places on your tour. You can have all kinds of fun skiing down the snowy slopes. There are lots of other sporty things to do too. But be careful that you don't bump into anyone.

There are kindergarten groups for children who are too young to ski. Spot two groups building snowmen.

Snowboarders use one wide board instead of two skis. Spot ten.

Snowboard

If you don't have your own skis, you can rent them. Find a ski-rental shop.

24

PRESENT CHECKLIST

Paraskiers ski off mountains and float to the ground using a parachute. Find three.

Teachers called ski instructors give people skiing lessons. Spot two.

You can go sliding down the slopes on a toboggan. Find nine.

On gentle slopes, a drag lift pulls you up to the top. Spot three people on a drag lift.

In the next place, you'll be doing lots of shopping. Find this useful shopping bag.

Some people go climbing up the mountains. Spot three climbers with ice picks.

Ice pick

On frozen lakes, you can skate and play sports. Spot 30 people on skates.

There are hang-gliders in the sky. Spot three.

On safari

Great Aunt Marigold is about to take a photo. Can you see her?

When they spot a dead animal, vultures fly down to feed on it. Can you find 14?

Baboons live in groups called troops. They all look after the babies. Find 23.

Baobab trees store lots of water in their trunks. Spot two.

Cheetahs creep up on other animals before chasing them. Find five.

Agama lizards scuttle around in the grass or on rocks. Spot three.

Here, you're out in the open air, on the hot, dry, African plains. You've joined lots of other people on an exciting animal-watching trip called a safari. It's hard to believe there are so many amazing animals living in one place.

Hot-air balloon

Bus

Truck

On a safari, you can travel around in different ways. Spot three of each of these.

Ostriches are the biggest birds in the world. They can't fly but they can run very fast. Find 15.

Insects called termites build nests inside huge mounds of soil. Find four termite mounds.

26

PRESENT CHECKLIST

Weaverbirds make complicated nests out of lots of pieces of grass. Spot ten.

Lions like to lie in the shade. Can you find nine?

Zebra

Thomson's gazelle

Wildebeest

These animals eat grass nearly all day long. Spot 15 of each of them.

Scientists come here to learn about wildlife. Can you spot four?

Wild dogs hunt together in groups called packs. Spot nine.

Elephants are so big, they need to eat a lot. Find 17.

Giraffes have to bend a long way down to reach water. Spot 13.

You're going to an even drier place next. Find a bottle of water to take with you.

Town life

Great Aunt Marigold is busy making friends. Can you see her?

At the New Year, some people dress up and parade along the street. Find a dragon costume.

Pigs

Ducks

Can you see these animals being taken to market?

In China, there are steam trains, and newer diesel or electric trains too. Spot a steam train.

Most Chinese people are farmers. Spot ten farmers growing rice in paddy fields.

In this pretty town, there's a canal to walk along and some lovely gardens. As you wander around, you'll see people getting ready for the New Year Festival. They are shopping for presents and making decorations.

Tea grows in lots of parts of China and is a popular drink. Spot some teapots for sale.

Most people travel around the town on bicycles. Find 20.

Silk thread comes from caterpillars called silkworms. People weave it into soft cloth. Find some rolls of silk cloth.

Giant pandas are very rare animals. Wild ones live only in China. Find a toy panda.

Some people keep birds. Find seven birdcages.

Find a group of people doing exercises called t'ai chi.

Many things are made out of bamboo. Can you find three of these bamboo baby buggies?

There will be lots of snow in the next place. Find a spade to clear a path.

A pagoda is a kind of tall tower. It's usually part of a temple. Can you see one?

Spot nine people carrying things in baskets hanging from a pole across their shoulders.

Find three kites.

Forest people

Great Aunt Marigold is sitting in the shade. Find her.

The Ashaninca travel up and down the river in canoes. They fish from them too. Find nine.

People paint their faces with red dye from the seeds of anatto plants. Spot a girl with an armful of anatto seeds.

Mothers often carry their babies in slings. Find nine babies in slings.

Many beautiful birds live in the forest. Some are kept as pets. Spot a girl with a pet parrot.

You've paddled up the River Amazon, right into the heart of the hot, sticky rainforest. The people living here are called the Ashaninca. They gather plants from the forest, hunt animals for food, and grow their own crops.

The main food is a plant called cassava, which is made into flour. Spot someone mashing up cassava with a pole.

Men go hunting with bows and arrows. Find 11 bows.

The big thatched roofs are made from palm leaves. Can you see someone mending a roof?

PRESENT CHECKLIST

Families of red howler monkeys live in the forest. Spot 18.

People sleep in hammocks. Can you find seven?

Wood is used to make houses, ladders, canoes, weapons and tools. Find someone chopping wood.

Children use catapults to shoot at birds. Find two.

Houses are built on stilts above the ground, so people use ladders to climb up to them. Spot two ladders.

The Ashaninca grow cotton to make clothes, hammocks and slings. Find two people doing each of these things.

Spinning cotton into thread

Weaving thread into cloth

Next, you're going to a big party. Find a feather garland to wear.

Island life

Great Aunt Marigold is busy exploring the island. Can you see where she is?

Donkeys are used for carrying things. Find eight.

Modern vases are often made to look like ancient Greek ones. Spot six big vases like this.

This musical instrument is a bouzouki. Can you find eight?

Stuffed vine leaves

Yogurt and banana

Greek salad

Restaurants serve delicious food. Spot someone eating this meal.

Churches often have dome-shaped roofs. Find three.

This pretty island looks like an exciting place to stop for a while. You can explore the winding alleyways or climb up to the old castle on the hill. There are lots of people here. Some live on the island and some are just visiting.

Women make lace and embroider cloths. They decorate their homes with these. Spot ten women sewing.

Leather bags

Can you see where these things are being sold?

Necklaces

Postcards

Cats wander along streets and over rooftops. They like to sleep in the sun. Spot 12.

32

You can learn about Greek history by visiting ruined buildings. Find some ruins.

The only way to leave the island is by boat. Can you spot five little boats with oars?

Mediterranean monk seals are so rare, they are hardly ever seen. Can you find two?

When they are closed, shutters keep houses cool. Spot 11 windows with red shutters.

In the next place, you'll see lots of animals. Find a pad and crayons to draw them.

Many islanders make money from fishing. Find four of each of these things.

Fishing boats

Can you spot these people working?

Shoemaker **Baker**

Baskets of fish

Tinsmith

On the street

Great Aunt Marigold is stuck in traffic. Can you see her?

Monkeys, called langurs, scamper around the town, looking for food. Can you find 20?

Trains are often so crowded that people have to sit on top. Spot one.

Cycle rickshaw

Scooter rickshaw

Rickshaws are used as taxis. Spot eight of each of these types.

To say "hello", you put your hands together and bow your head. Spot 12 pairs of people saying hello.

You've arrived in the middle of the hustle and bustle of an Indian town. The streets are full of traffic and swarming with crowds. Plenty of rich people live here, but other people are so poor, they have to beg for money.

The old fort was built hundreds of years ago, to protect the town from enemies. Can you see it?

Tea is boiled in a pan with milk and sugar. Spices are often added. Spot the tea seller.

Can you spot 16 crows?

PRESENT CHECKLIST

The cinema is very popular. Find this poster telling people what's on.

Can you see where these tasty sweetmeats are being sold?

The street barber doesn't charge much to shave people. Find him.

A puri is a type of bread which is fried until it puffs up into a ball. Spot a man frying puris.

In the next place, the ground might be wet. Find a pair of deck shoes so you don't slip.

To worship, Hindus go to temples and Muslims go to mosques. Find one of each.

Temple

Mosque

Most Indians are Hindus. They believe that cows are holy, so let them wander wherever they want. Spot seven cows.

Reindeer races

Great Aunt Marigold is admiring the reindeer. Can you see her?

Dogs called laikas are used to pull sleds. Their thick coats keep them warm. Spot 32.

Balalaika

Accordion

Musicians entertain people at the races. Spot six of each of these musical instruments.

People fill oil drums with ice from the river. They melt it for water. Spot 20.

The nearest train station and airport are far away, so people often arrive by helicopter. Can you spot two?

You've journeyed all the way north to Siberia. Everyone is celebrating the end of the long, cold winter with reindeer races on the frozen river. Many people here keep herds of reindeer. They make warm clothes from their skins.

Some herders follow their reindeer around as they look for food. They live in tents called chums. Find three.

Frozen rivers make good ice rinks. Can you spot 15 people skating?

There are huge forests in Siberia, so people make many things out of wood. Spot three people chopping wood.

A samovar is a big metal pot for making tea. Can you see one?

Reindeer herders carve beautiful things from bone. Can you see someone carving?

Wild bears, wolves, elk and sable live in nearby forests. Find a toy bear.

Sliding along on skis is often easier than walking on snow. Spot ten people on skis.

The next place is cold and snowy too. Find some warm, furry ear muffs.

Trucks are good for driving on icy ground. Snowmobiles are used for shorter journeys. Find six of each.

Snowmobile

Truck

For the races, reindeer wear bright cloths and harnesses. Find someone dressing up his reindeer.

Muffin seems to like her yellow cushion. See if you can spot her.

Baby Nina is munching her bananas. Can you find her?

Great Aunt Eva loves her garland of flowers. Can you see where she is?

A painted parasol was just what Rosie wanted. Can you see her?

Cruising along

Can you find Mr. Choy trying on his white furry hat?

The last part of your Great World Tour is a trip on this luxury cruise ship. There are lots of things to do on board.

As a surprise, Great Aunt Marigold has invited all your friends and relations. Can you spot them with their presents?

Can you spot Jack with his bath salts?

Jo is keeping cool with her fan. Find her.

Uncle Mike is looking out to sea through his blue binoculars. Can you find him?

38

Great Uncle Frank is already eating his chocolates. Can you see where he is?

Aunt Mimi is having fun with her green flippers. Look hard and see if you can spot her.

Max is wearing his new T-shirt to play with some friends. Find him.

Spot Doctor Parekh chatting to someone about her clay statue.

Find the twins listening to their radio together.

Spot Sacha showing off his striped gloves.

Lennox is nibbling his cheese. Can you spot him?

Mrs. Choy is very pleased with her mirror. Can you see where she is?

Sniff is playing with his spotted ball. Find him.

Your tour is over! To say "thank you" to Great Aunt Marigold, you've bought her a new dress. Can you see her wearing it?

39

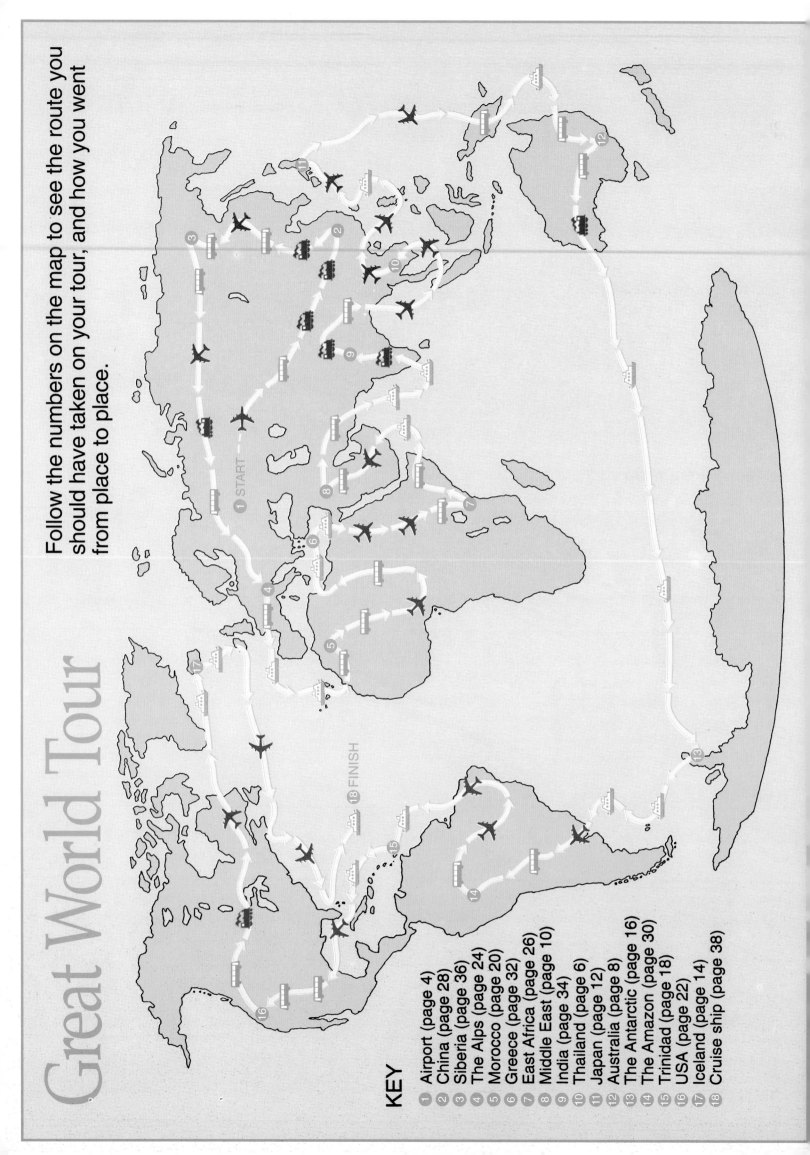

Great World Tour

Follow the numbers on the map to see the route you should have taken on your tour, and how you went from place to place.

① START

⑱ FINISH

KEY

1 Airport (page 4)
2 China (page 28)
3 Siberia (page 36)
4 The Alps (page 24)
5 Morocco (page 20)
6 Greece (page 32)
7 East Africa (page 26)
8 Middle East (page 10)
9 India (page 34)
10 Thailand (page 6)
11 Japan (page 12)
12 Australia (page 8)
13 The Antarctic (page 16)
14 The Amazon (page 30)
15 Trinidad (page 18)
16 USA (page 22)
17 Iceland (page 14)
18 Cruise ship (page 38)

Extra puzzle

To do this puzzle, you'll need to look back through the book. Don't forget to look at the blue strips at the top of each double page. If you get stuck, you'll find the answers on page 48.

1. Which was the coldest place you visited?

2. Which was the hottest place you visited?

3. What was the earliest time you had to get up?

4. Which place were you in at 3.30 pm?

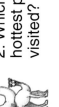

5. How many snowy places did you visit?

6. How many sunny places did you visit?

7. How many of each of these did you go on?

8. Which of these buildings is a hotel?

A   B   C   D   E   F

9. Which of these people saves other people's lives?

A   B   C   D   E   F   G

10. Which of these might be offered to you in the middle of a desert?

A   B   C   D   E   F

11. Which of these people is trying to keep the sun off his or her face?

A   B   C   D   E   F

41

At the airport 4-5

Screens
1 2 3 4 5 6
7 8 9 10 11
Person buying
sunglasses
12
Covered
walkway
13
Person eating
meal
14
Buggies
15 16
Cat
17
Bag being
searched
18
Knife on X-ray
machine
19
Person going
through metal
detector
20
Phones
21 22 23 24
25 26 27 28
Flight attendants
29 30 31 32 33
34 35 36 37 38
Control tower
39

Red flag
40
Bureau de
change
41
Trolleys
42 43 44 45
46 47 48
Person with torn
ticket
49
Cargo hold
50
Big box of
chocolates
51
Great Aunt
Marigold
52

Floating market 6-7

Boats selling hats
1 2
Weighing scales
3 4 5 6 7
8 9 10 11
Purple-throated
sunbirds
12 13 14 15
16 17 18 19
20 21 22
Boats selling
cooked food
23 24
Corn on the cob
seller
25
Boats full of
watermelons
26 27
Boats full of
coconuts
28 29
Boats full of
pineapples
30 31
Boats full of limes
32 33
Wooden table
34
Embroidered
cushions
35
Silver necklaces
36

Lacquerware
ducks
37
Buddhist monks
38 39 40
41 42 43
Silk jacket
44
Buddhist temple
45
Boats selling fish
46 47 48
Boats selling
pots and pans
49 50 51
Boats selling
flowers
52 53 54
Dolls
55
Painted parasol
56
Great Aunt
Marigold
57

On the beach 8-9

Sailboards
1 2 3 4 5
6 7 8 9 10
People putting
on sunblock
11 12 13 14
Dolphins
15 16 17 18 19
20 21 22 23 24
Kayaks
25 26 27 28 29
30 31
Speedboats
32 33 34 35 36
37 38
Sailboats
39 40 41 42 43
44 45
Seagulls
46 47 48 49 50
51 52 53 54 55
56 57 58 59
Water-skiers
60 61 62 63 64
65 66 67
Lifesaver team
68
Divers
69 70 71 72 73
Snorkels
74 75 76 77 78
79 80 81 82 83
Parasailers
84 85

Camera
86
Jet skis
87 88 89 90 91
92 93 94 95
Surfboards
96 97 98 99 100
101 102 103 104
105 106 107 108
109 110 111 112
113 114 115 116
117 118 119 120
121 122 123 124
125
Toy koala
126
Toy kangaroo
127
Flags
128 129
Green flippers
130
Great Aunt
Marigold
131

42

Desert homes 10-11

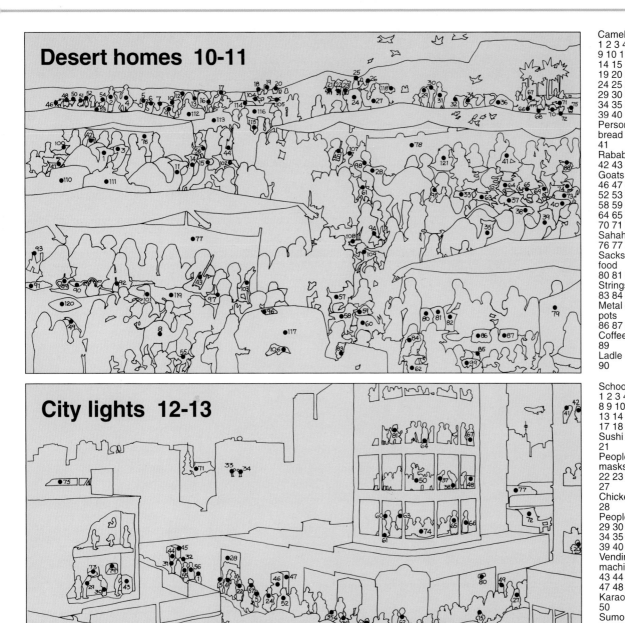

Camels	**Coffee cups**
1 2 3 4 5 6 7 8	91
9 10 11 12 13	**Pestle and**
14 15 16 17 18	**mortar**
19 20 21 22 23	92
24 25 26 27 28	**Camel saddles**
29 30 31 32 33	93 94 95
34 35 36 37 38	**Book**
39 40	96
Person baking	**Bowls of camel**
bread	**milk**
41	97 98 99
Rababs	**Salukis**
42 43 44 45	100 101 102 103
Goats	104 105 106 107
46 47 48 49 50 51	108 109
52 53 54 55 56 57	**Trucks**
58 59 60 61 62 63	110 111 112 113
64 65 66 67 68 69	114 115 116 117
70 71 72 73 74 75	118
Sahahs	**Rug**
76 77 78 79	119
Sacks of dried	**Yellow cushion**
food	120
80 81 82	**Great Aunt**
Strings of onions	**Marigold**
83 84 85	121
Metal cooking	
pots	
86 87 88	
Coffee pot	
89	
Ladle	
90	

City lights 12-13

Schoolchildren	**Towel**
1 2 3 4 5 6 7	73
8 9 10 11 12	**Traditional**
13 14 15 16	**restaurant**
17 18 19 20	74
Sushi for sale	**Bullet trains**
21	75 76 77
People wearing	**Place selling**
masks	**computers**
22 23 24 25 26	78
27	**Person asleep**
Chicken stall	79
28	**Radio**
People bowing	80
29 30 31 32 33	**Great Aunt**
34 35 36 37 38	**Marigold**
39 40 41 42	81
Vending	
machines	
43 44 45 46	
47 48 49	
Karaoke bar	
50	
Sumo wrestlers	
51 52 53 54	
Kimonos	
55 56 57 58 59	
60 61 62 63 64	
65 66 67 68 69	
70	
Temple	
71	
Shrine	
72	

At the pool 14-15

Eider ducks	**Waitresses**
1 2 3 4 5 6 7	80 81 82 83
8 9 10 11 12	**People with mud**
13 14 15 16	**on their faces**
17 18 19 20	84 85 86 87 88
Toy sharks	89 90 91 92 93
21 22 23 24 25	94 95 96 97 98
26 27	**Sea-sickness**
Inflatable beds	**pills**
28 29 30 31 32	99
33 34	**Man arriving at**
Buoys	**hotel**
35 36 37 38 39	100
40 41 42 43 44	**Women's**
45 46 47 48 49	**changing rooms**
50 51 52 53 54	101
Pipes blowing	**Food trays**
out steam	102 103 104 105
55 56 57 58 59	106 107 108 109
People horse	110 111 112 113
riding	114 115 116 117
60 61 62 63 64	118 119 120 121
65 66	122
People hiking	**Trucks**
67 68 69 70 71	123 124 125 126
72 73	127 128 129 130
Doctor	**Bath salts**
74	131
Person who has	**Great Aunt**
bought face	**Marigold**
cream	132
75	
Waiters	
76 77 78 79	

Frozen land 16-17

Albatrosses	Satellite tags
1 2 3	57 58
Research station	Flashlight
4	59
Killer whales	Leopard seals
5 6 7 8	60 61
Castle iceberg	Dinghies
9	62 63 64 65 66
Pyramid iceberg	67 68 69
10	Humpback whale
Greek temple	70
iceberg	Planes
11	71 72 73
Penguins	Striped gloves
porpoising	74
12 13 14 15 16	Great Aunt
17 18 19 20 21	Marigold
22 23	75
Penguins	
tobogganing	
24 25 26 27 28	
29 30 31 32 33	
34 35	
Divers	
36 37 38 39 40	
41 42	
Crabeater seals	
43 44 45 46 47	
48 49 50 51 52	
53 54	
Cruise ship	
55	
Research ship	
56	

Carnival! 18-19

Great Aunt	Jab Molassi
Marigold	16
1	Burroquite
Underwater	17
group	Moco Jumbie
2	18
Circus group	Pans
3	19 20 21 22 23
Incas group	24 25 26 27 28
4	29 30 31 32 33
Spanish dancing	34 35 36
group	Floats
5	37 38 39
Flying animals	Policemen
group	40 41 42 43 44
6	45 46 47 48 49
Fruit sorbet	Amazing
7	costume
Corn on the cob	50
8	T-shirt
Roti	51
9	
Person	
pretending to be	
a judge	
10	
Coconut seller	
11	
People singing	
12 13	
Fruit stall	
14	
Calculator	
15	

Shady souk 20-21

Herbs and	Shady hat
spices	34
1	Olives
Lute	35
2	People
Drum	bargaining
3	36 37
People carrying	Chickens
wool	38 39 40 41 42
4 5 6	43 44 45 46
Dates for sale	Water carriers
7	47 48 49 50
Copper trays	Mirror
8	51
Painted pottery	Great Aunt
9	Marigold
Leather slippers	52
10	
Woven baskets	
11	
Embroidered	
caps	
12	
Saddles	
13 14	
Glasses of mint	
tea	
15 16 17 18 19	
20 21	
Cedarwood	
containers	
22 23 24 25 26	
27 28 29 30 31	
32 33	

At the mall 22-23

Benches
1 2 3 4 5 6 7 8
Information desk
9
Lost child
10
Hair salon
11
Kites
12
Sports
equipment
13
Books
14
Cowboy hats
15
Shoes
16
Jeans
17
Flowers
18
Cakes
19
Group of
cheerleaders
20
Ice cream
21
Spaghetti
22
Pizza
23

Flamingo statues
24 25 26 27 28
29 30 31 32 33
34 35 36 37 38
39 40 41 42 43
44 45 46 47
Suitcase
48
Security guards
49 50 51 52 53
54 55 56 57 58
Telephones
59 60 61 62 63
Glass elevator
64
Mural
65
Spotted ball
66
Great Aunt
Marigold
67

Going skiing 24-25

Snowmobiles
1 2 3 4 5
Broken goggles
6
Chairlifts
7 8 9 10
Gondolas
11 12 13 14
Sleighs
15 16 17
Groups building
snowmen
18 19
Snowboarders
20 21 22 23 24
25 26 27 28 29
Ski-rental shop
30
Climbers
31 32 33
People on skates
34 35 36 37 38
39 40 41 42 43
44 45 46 47 48
49 50 51 52 53
54 55 56 57 58
59 60 61 62 63
Hang-gliders
64 65 66
Shopping bag
67
People on drag
lift
68 69 70

Toboggans
71 72 73 74 75
76 77 78 79
Ski instructors
80 81
Paraskiers
82 83 84
Cheese
85
Great Aunt
Marigold
86

On safari 26-27

Vultures
1 2 3 4 5 6 7 8 9
10 11 12 13 14
Baboons
15 16 17 18 19
20 21 22 23 24
25 26 27 28 29
30 31 32 33 34
35 36 37
Baobab trees
38 39
Cheetahs
40 41 42 43 44
Agama lizards
45 46 47
Hot-air balloons
48 49 50
Buses
51 52 53
Trucks
54 55 56
Ostriches
57 58 59 60 61
62 63 64 65 66
67 68 69 70 71
Termite mounds
72 73 74 75
Wild dogs
76 77 78 79 80
81 82 83 84
Elephants 85 86
87 88 89 90 91
92 93 94 95 96
97 98 99 100 101

Giraffes 102 103
104 105 106 107
108 109 110 111
112 113 114
Water bottle 115
Scientists
116 117 118 119
Wildebeest
120 121 122 123
124 125 126 127
128 129 130 131
132 133 134
Thomson's
gazelles
135 136 137 138
139 140 141 142
143 144 145 146
147 148 149
Zebras
150 151 152 153
154 155 156 157
158 159 160 161
162 163 164
Lions 165 166
167 168 169 170
171 172 173
Weaverbirds
174 175 176 177
178 179 180 181
182 183
Blue binoculars
184
Great Aunt
Marigold 185

Town life 28-29

Dragon costume
1
Pigs
2
Ducks
3
Steam train
4
Farmers
5 6 7 8 9 10
11 12 13 14
Teapots for sale
15
Bicycles
16 17 18 19 20
21 22 23 24 25
26 27 28 29 30
31 32 33 34 35
Rolls of silk cloth
36
Pagoda
37
People with
baskets on poles
38 39 40 41 42
43 44 45 46
Kites
47 48 49
Spade
50
Baby buggies
51 52 53
T'ai chi group
54

Birdcages
55 56 57 58 59
60 61
Toy panda
62
Wooden fan
63
Great Aunt
Marigold
64

Forest people 30-31

Canoes
1 2 3 4 5
6 7 8 9
Girl with anatto
seeds
10
Babies in slings
11 12 13 14 15
16 17 18 19
Girl with parrot
20
Person mashing
up cassava
21
Bows
22 23 24 25 26
27 28 29 30 31
32
Person mending
roof
33
Ladders
34 35
People weaving
36 37
People spinning
38 39
Feather garland
40
Catapults
41 42
Person chopping
wood
43

Hammocks
44 45 46 47 48
49 50
Red howler
monkeys
51 52 53 54 55
56 57 58 59 60
61 62 63 64 65
66 67 68
Bunch of
bananas
69
Great Aunt
Marigold
70

Island life 32-33

Donkeys
1 2 3 4 5
6 7 8
Vases
9 10 11 12 13 14
Bouzoukis
15 16 17 18 19
20 21 22
Person eating
meal
23
Churches
24 25 26
Women sewing
27 28 29 30 31
32 33 34 35 36
Necklaces
37
Postcards
38
Leather bags
39
Cats
40 41 42 43 44
45 46 47 48 49
50 51
Baskets of fish
52 53 54 55
Fishing boats
56 57 58 59
Tinsmith
60
Baker
61

Shoemaker
62
Pad and crayons
63
Windows with
red shutters
64 65 66 67 68
69 70 71 72 73
74
Mediterranean
monk seals
75 76
Boats with oars
77 78 79 80 81
Ruins
82
Clay statue
83
Great Aunt
Marigold
84

46

On the street 34-35

Reindeer races 36-37

Cruising along 38-39

Langurs
1 2 3 4 5 6 7
8 9 10 11 12
13 14 15 16
17 18 19 20
Train
21
Cycle rickshaws
22 23 24 25 26
27 28 29
Scooter
rickshaws
30 31 32 33 34
35 36 37
Pairs of people
saying hello
38 39 40 41 42
43 44 45 46 47
48 49
Old fort
50
Tea seller
51
Crows
52 53 54 55 56
57 58 59 60 61
62 63 64 65 66
67
Mosque
68
Temple
69
Cows 70 71 72
73 74 75 76 77

Deck shoes
78
Man frying puris
79
Street barber
80
Sweetmeats
81
Cinema poster
82
Garland of
flowers
83
Great Aunt
Marigold
84

Laikas
1 2 3 4 5 6 7
8 9 10 11 12
13 14 15 16
17 18 19 20
21 22 23 24
25 26 27 28
29 30 31 32
Balalaikas
33 34 35 36 37
38
Accordions
39 40 41 42 43
44
Oil drums
45 46 47 48 49
50 51 52 53 54
55 56 57 58 59
60 61 62 63 64
Helicopters
65 66
Chums
67 68 69
People skating
70 71 72 73 74
75 76 77 78 79
80 81 82 83 84
People chopping
wood 85 86 87
Trucks 88 89 90
91 92 93
Snowmobiles
94 95 96 97 98
99

Person dressing
up reindeer
100
Ear muffs
101
People on skis
102 103 104 105
106 107 108 109
110 111
Toy bear
112
Person carving
113
Samovar
114
White furry hat
115
Great Aunt
Marigold
116

Muffin 1
Baby Nina 2
Great Aunt Eva 3
Rosie 4
Jack 5
Jo 6
Uncle Mike 7
Mrs. Choy 8
Sniff 9
Great Aunt
Marigold 10
Lennox 11
Sacha 12
The twins 13
Doctor Parekh
14
Max 15
Aunt Mimi 16
Great Uncle
Frank 17
Mr. Choy 18

47

Acknowledgements

The publishers would like to thank the following organizations and individuals for their help in the preparation of this book:

pages 4 – 5: Roz Quade, BAA London Gatwick, England

pages 8 – 9: Australian Tourist Commission, London, England

pages 10 – 11: Shelagh Weir, Curator for the Middle East, Museum of Mankind (British Museum), London, England

pages 12 – 13: Ms Mitsuko Ohno

pages 14 – 15: Blue Lagoon Ltd, PO Box 22, 240 Grindavik, Iceland

pages 16 – 17: Sheila Anderson

pages 18 – 19: Trinidad High Commissioner's Office, London, England

pages 20 – 21: The Best of Morocco

pages 24 – 25: David Hearns, Ski Club of Great Britain, London, England

pages 26 – 27: David Duthie

pages 28 – 29: Frances Wood, Curator of the Chinese Collections, British Library, London, England

pages 30 – 31: Survival International, 11-15 Emerald Street, London WC1N 3QL, England, UK. For more information about Rainforest people, please contact Survival International

pages 32 – 33: Andrew Stoddart, The Hellenic Bookservice, 91 Fortress Road, London NW5 1AG, England

pages 34 – 35: A.K. Singh, Indian Tourist Board, London, England

pages 36 – 37: Dr Alan Wood, University of Lancaster, England

pages 38 – 39: Tim Stocker, P&O Cruises, 77 New Oxford Street, London WC1A 1PP, England

Answers to Extra puzzle on page 41:

1. Siberia

2. East Africa

3. 8 a.m. (Thailand)

4. Airport

5. Three (The Antarctic, The Alps, Siberia)

6. Five (Middle East, Trinidad, Morocco, East Africa, Greece)

7. 18 boats; 20 planes; 8 trains; 22 buses

8. D

9. F

10. C

11. F

ISBN 0-439-12055-1

First published in Great Britain in 1996 by Usborne Publishing Ltd.
Copyright © 1996 by Usborne Publishing Ltd.
All rights reserved.
Published by Scholastic Inc., 555 Broadway, New York, NY 10012,
by arrangement with Usborne Publishing Ltd.
SCHOLASTIC and associated logos are trademarks and/or registered trademarks of Scholastic Inc.

12 11 10 9 8 7 6 5 4 3 2   9/9 0 1 2 3 4/0

Printed in the U.S.A.   08

First Scholastic printing, October 1999

The name Usborne and the device 🎈 are Trade Marks of Usborne Publishing Ltd.

Look 🚢 🚂 Puzzle ✈ 🚌 Learn

The Great World Tour

Great Aunt Marigold has given you a wonderful present - a ticket for a Great World Tour. As you go on your exciting trip around the world, there are puzzles to solve, presents to look for and clues to help you find out where to go next. A snowy ski resort in the Alps, a bustling shopping mall in the USA, a Bedouin encampment in a hot, dry desert, and a crowded Australian beach – these are just a few of the places you will visit. As well as providing countless hours of puzzle-solving fun, **The Great World Tour** is packed with fascinating facts about people and places. If you get really stuck trying to find the hidden things, all the answers are at the back of the book.

Temple
1

Dancing dolls
2

Person cooking
3

Purple-throated sunbirds
4 5 6 7 8 9

Boat selling hats
10

Baskets of fish
11 12 13

Corn on the cob stall
14

Embroidered cushions
15 16

Boats full of fruits
17 18

Boat selling pots and pans
19

Parasol
20

Here's the answer to the puzzle on the front of the book.

This edition is only available for distribution through the school market.

SCHOLASTIC INC.

0-439-12055-1